Usborne
Little First Colouring

Garden

Illustrated by Jenny Brown

Words by Kirsteen Robson

A bird sings
loudly.

A cat purrs
softly.

Busy ants

A ladybird
resting

A frog croaks.

An owl hoots.

A fox has a bushy tail.

A hedgehog
has prickles.

A millipede has
lots of legs.

A spider has
eight legs.

A mouse
scurries around.

A snail slides
along.

A bee on a flower

A wasp on
a strawberry

A sunflower
is yellow.

A poppy
is red.

A grasshopper
jumps.

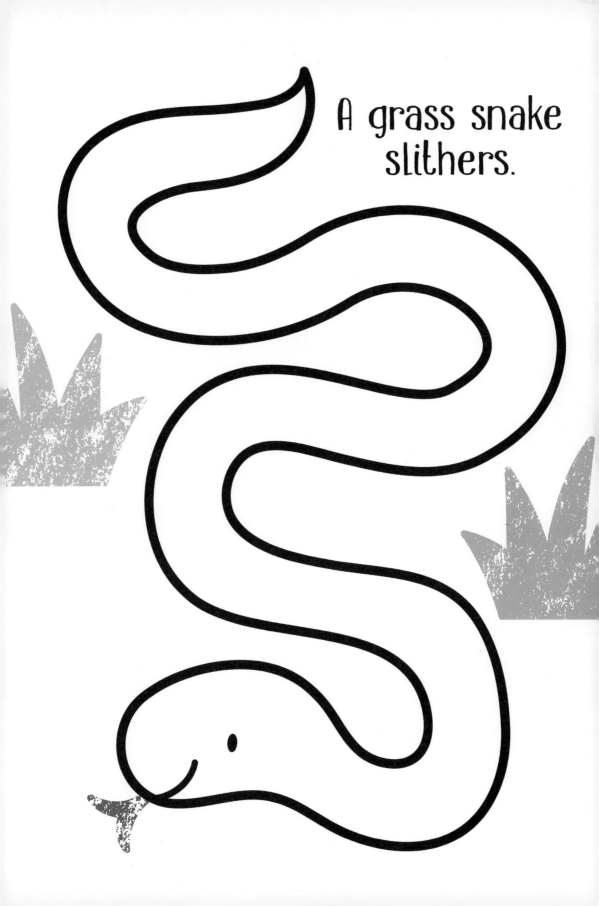

A grass snake slithers.

A butterfly flies in the day.

A bat flies
at night.

A tree is green
in summer.

An autumn tree is orange and red.

A slug eating
a mushroom

A rabbit
eating
grass

A worm
wriggles along.

A toad
crawls.

A squirrel
in a tree

A mole in the
ground

An aphid is
    green.

A beetle is
black.

A woodlouse
likes dark
places.